GW00646810
groovy chick
£6.99

personal details

name Béanín Smith

age 13

telephone 028 30 878 919

email

my favourite friend is Tara

my top hobby is Drama + Swimming

Gadd House, Arcadia Avenue
London, N3 2JU

Printed in China

contents

Hi!

Welcome back! I can't believe this is my third annual! I had a great year and hope you did too. My mates and I have put together a whole bunch of cool ideas and stuff to do. Check out the fashion and shopping tips, our bedroom makeover, film club and party ideas. Plus I have a bunch of new friends for you to meet!

Love,

groovy chick

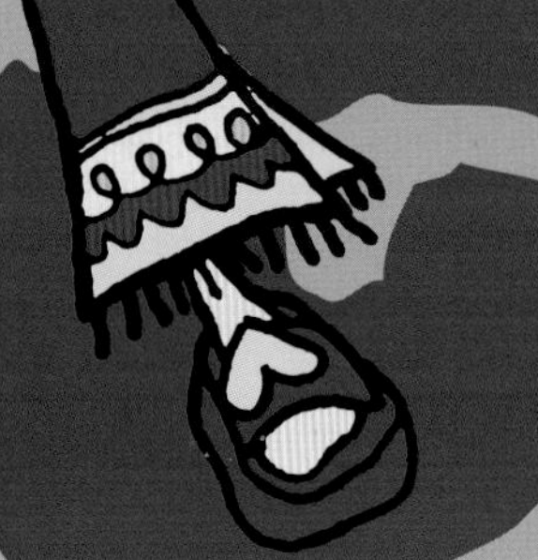

Do you know the names of some of my best mates?

1: starlet, 2: hi sweetie, 3: trés chic, 4: football babe, 5: hey gorgeous, 6: dj babe, 7: pop princess, 8: whoops, 9: party girl, 10: bling bling

one of my fave photos of the year
what are your fave memories of the past year?
my groovy
my nicknames:
my best friends: Eimear, Eilidh, Sammy, Cathy, Katie
my school: Our Lady's Grammar
my teacher: Miss Gilmore
my year:
CD
CD

my favourite:

colour: pink & blue

book:

outfit:

song:

hairstyle: Straight

pop star:

film: Nemo

film star:

tv show: Corrie

2005

another fave photo from the year

groovy chick's
travel journal
last year I
went to: the
Costa del Sol
a sketch of my fave place
my favourite part of the
holiday was: the Shopping centres +
water park
my fave photo
10

groovy chick loves her holidays. Where was your last vacation? Fill in **groovy chick**'s journal to remember your best trip, or take it with you on your next hol!

Answers: 1. Paris 2. London 3. Egypt 4. South America 5. Scotland

groovy goals

Every year **groovy chick** makes a list of goals, and tries her very best to achieve them. Write down your three goals for the coming year ... anything you like!

hi sweetie's style file

groovy chick's fave fashionista pal, **hi sweetie**, has some top tips to share. Just turn the page!

shopping strategy

Ever go shopping and end up buying something you never wear? It's easy to get all crazy over a super cool top, only to discover it doesn't match anything you have at home. Here is hi sweetie's advice: Before hitting the shops, check out your closet. On a piece of paper make three columns: one for things you **must have** (and in which colours), the second for things that would be great to have but aren't fashion emergencies and the last for things that are pure luxury.

Use the list to guide you through the racks at the shops – don't get distracted by something that isn't on the 'must have' list (unless it's an irresistible bargain, of course!)

Don't forget!

Make sure everything you buy can go with more than one outfit!

on a budget?

Not a problem, just get creative! First step: mix and match your existing clothes to create new outfits.

Try these:

Pair skintight black leggings with a short skirt, add boots and voila! A 'new' outfit!

Layer a long-sleeved t-shirt or polo neck under a short-sleeved tee for a trendy top!

Remove boring buttons from a cardigan and replace them with cool beaded ones!

second-hand with style

Vintage shops, charity shops or street markets all have cool and original gear that won't break the piggy bank.

- Sparkly beaded brooches or pins and scarves really spice up an outfit.
- Ribbons are super cheap and make great belts; turn to page 33 and make your own!
- Go for a funky hat and big shades for that 'celeb incognito' look
- Denim and leather goods, which are normally really expensive, are much cheaper second hand.

fave looks

cool caps
the poncho
teeny clutch bags
ribbon belts
ruffle skirts
furry boots

of the year

Note your hot tips of the past year, or draw your fave outfit ...

Pink at heart loves ... You guessed it... pink !
And it does suit her! Different colours compliment different skin tones and hair colours. Which colours work best for you
what's your colour?
warm or cool?
From your skin, hair and eye colour combination you can tell if you are warm or cool.
warm combos:
creamy, peachy or bronze tone skin
green, deep blue, hazel or brown eyes
golden, strawberry blonde, copper, chestnut or dark brown hair
Best colours for warm:
cream or ivory, rose pink, powder blue, scarlet, peach, gold, chocolate or mauve

what do your fave shades say about yourpersonality?
blue: You're clever, keep your cool under pressure, you don't waste time on gossip.
yellow: You're usually totally happy, always up for something new and great at making others laugh.
pink: You're super affectionate and loving, you always give people a second chance.
black: You like to chill and have time to think. You might be quiet in a big group, but your best friends know the real you!
red: You're fun-loving, super smart, strong and a born leader. You might be a bit bossy sometimes!
green: You're honest, love the outdoors and like to look after other people.
cool combos:
blue, grey, blue-green or dark brown eyes
pale blonde, dark blonde, brown, dark brown or black hair
milky white, rosy, olive or dark tone skin
Best colours for cool: white, pale pink, baby blue, lilac, purple, cherry red, silver, deep aqua

beauty stop

whether you're getting ready for a holiday or a party at your mate's, hey gorgeous always has some cool tips to help you look your best ...

nail news

1. Don't polish nails in the sun; the heat will cause the polish to bubble
2. Always wipe even bare nails with polish remover before polishing, to get them super clean
3. Don't shake the polish bottle, this creates bubbles; roll it between your hands instead
4. When applying a dark shade, use a basecoat first; dark colours will make your nails yellow

alligator skin?

Getting ready to hit the beach? Then it might be time to exfoliate... as in 'out with the old, in with the new'. Make your own body scrub by mixing 1/4 cup sugar, two tablespoons olive oil and two tablespoons of milk. Gently rub the mixture on your body while standing in the shower, and rinse off with warm water. Follow up with a rich body moisturiser.

perfect pedi

1. Remove old nail polish. Fill a pan with warm water and add some bubble bath. Soak for ten minutes then remove and dry your feet.
2. Using toenail clippers, cut your nails straight across. Then file across to smooth out any rough edges.
3. Apply a scrub (you can use the body scrub recipe opposite), concentrating on the heels and balls of your feet.
4. Dry your feet really well and massage in some moisturising lotion.
5. Apply nail polish remover on a cotton ball to wipe away any lotion. Weave a tissue between your toes to keep them separated and free from smudging. Then... get painting! Wear a toe ring or two for extra style!

hair rescue

1. Fight off the frizz... rub a small blob of hair gel in your hands and run your fingers through wet hair; let your hair air dry if you have time.
2. Hair too thick... ask your stylist for some layers to make it less heavy; a dab of shampoo run through when your hair's still wet will calm down the frizzies.
3. Thin hair – use a volumizing shampoo, not too much conditioner and blow-dry upside down.
4. Get more shine... rinse hair with cool water after shampooing and conditioning.
5. Avoid breaking hair by patting it dry with a towel rather than rubbing, and don't put hair in a ponytail until it's dry.

'I'm a star' party

For your next party with the girls (and guys!) throw a star-studded event: dress up as your fave celeb!

1. Plan the big 'do' well in advance so all your mates can make it.
2. Design and make your own invitations. Don't forget all the important info like date and time, and of course, the theme! Film or pop stars only!
3. Get cracking in the kitchen. Stars need their nibbles! Have fun with the whole star theme – like star-shaped cookies, and you can even get star-shaped ice cube trays.
4. If the parents OK it, ask them if you can borrow a camera and have a real star-studded photo shoot as your guests arrive.
5. Sort the tunes. Maybe some of your pop star guests will lip sync to a few of their tracks!

Before the day of the party, find out which celebs your mates have chosen. Then plan an awards ceremony to take place at the end of the night.

Set up a nominations list and ask guests to write down their choice for each category.

make a star award

Using some thick card, draw star shapes for each award and cut them out. Colour both sides with a gold sparkly pen. Write the name of the award in black felt tip on one side.

Don't forget to read out the nominations for each category, then choose the winner based on the best outfit!

start a film club with groovy chick

a great excuse to meet up with your mates and chill ...

1. Invite a small group of friends to join the club and decide on meeting perhaps once or twice a month. Email everyone with the date and time of the first meeting.

2. Before the first meeting, ask everyone to send you a list of their fave movies. Write out all the film suggestions in alphabetical order. The first one on the list will be your first film.

3. As the host of the first meeting, you should rent or borrow the DVD or video, and provide the nibbles of course! Each meeting can be held at a different friend's house.

4. Make sure everyone has a comfy seat. Sit back and enjoy the film!

5. Start chatting about the film – the hostess should begin by summarising the story, then describe why she did or didn't like it. A good hostess should also encourage everyone to participate and calm down any heated debates!

6. Leave time at the end of the meeting to discuss the next film on the list and choose the next hostess.

other stuff
to talk about:
what was special (or not) about the story
which characters you liked or disliked
what was good or bad about the ending
what might happen in a sequel
find more films:
ask members to bring more suggestions
ask your family or teachers for ideas
my film facts:
my fave film ever: ....
the worst film I ever saw: ....
my fave actor: ....
my fave actress: Julia Roberts

groovy chick's
dream
bedroom
If you're like
groovy chick, you'll
be thinking pink, pink
pink and more pink!
Use this (or another
fave colour) as your base
and build from there
to create your
dream space.
note
Be sure to get your
parents' permission before
making over your room.
You will probably need
their help with some of
the projects to make
sure they turn out
super groovy!
26

walls

If you can't paint your room, stencils are a cheap and easy way to add some grooviness to those big bare walls. Turn to page 61 to find out how to make your own stencils.

bedding

Add comfy cushions to compliment your duvet and colour scheme. You might be lucky enough to find cool heart- or star-shaped ones! Look for interesting textures like fake fur, baubles or woven fabric. Turn to page 33 to make your own cushions!

furniture

If the parents allow it, you could transform your furniture with paint and/or more stencilling. Stamping is an easy way to get the same effect as stencilling but with smaller designs. You can buy different shaped sponges and rubber stamps at craft shops. Simply dip them in paint and press lightly onto a clean surface.

accessories & displays

Customise photo frames by gluing on your own artwork. You can do this with storage pots and boxes too. If you love glitter (and who doesn't?!), spread on a thin layer of glue and sprinkle!

Use this space to design your new room.

Fill it with sketches, colours and a list of ideas and things to do.

cool crafts with the girls

Groovy chick and her mates love to make things! Here are some of their latest ideas for decorating, making jewellery and other neat stuff. Ask an adult to help with any cutting. You can find all the things you need in craft shops and big department stores.

Think about colours and the designs you want, like hearts, stars or flowers, and decide where to put them; perhaps in a funky pattern on one wall, or in a row all around the room.

Turn to page 61 for sample stencils you can cut out.

groovy chick's stencils

1. Ask your parents to help you buy some emulsion paint, you will also need a bowl and a sponge and at least 6 pieces of A4 size card.
2. Draw your designs onto a piece of card.
3. Carefully cut out the shape, and the frame is your stencil; make 5 more.
4. Tape the stencils to your walls (use low-tac tape like masking tape).
5. Pour some paint into a bowl and dip one side of a sponge lightly into the paint; you don't need too much.
6. Dab the sponge on the cut-out part of the stencil, on the wall.
7. Leave the paint to dry for a few minutes, then carefully peel off the stencil frame.
8. Stand back and admire your work!
9. Clean up the mess!

Check out my cool stencil!

beach babe's towel

① cover the work area or floor with newspapers!

you will need

- 1 white beach towel
- fabric paints – any colours you like!
- shaped craft sponges (animals, flowers, hearts, stars)
- old newspapers

② Lay the towel flat over the newspaper. If you are using a new towel, be sure to wash it first so it won't be stiff.

③ Gently dip your sponges into the paint (not too much paint) and sponge them onto your towel in different places.

④ If you are allowed, you may place your hand and feet prints on the towel too!

⑤ Let it dry completely – for at least an hour.

⑥ Clean up your mess!

⑦ Plan your next beach or pool trip!

you will need:

- 8 pieces of thin ribbon 2.5 metres long
- 1 curtain ring
- glue stick
- 8 beads

bling bling belt

1. while holding the 8 ribbons together, hanging down, fold them in half.
2. Tie one set of ends to a curtain ring – tie two bunches of four ribbons so that two even lengths hang down.
3. Knot a bead to each of the other ends.
4. wrap the belt around your hips and loop the beaded ribbon ends back through the ring twice.

crazy cushions by go girl

you will need:
fleece fabric in assorted colours, pen, ruler, scissors, craft glue, cotton wool, felt fabric in assorted colours, sequins

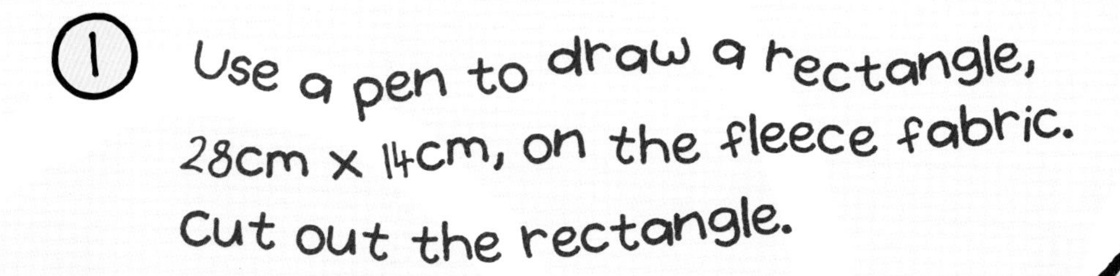

1. Use a pen to draw a rectangle, 28cm x 14cm, on the fleece fabric. Cut out the rectangle.
2. Fold the fabric in half and glue along two edges. Leave to dry.
3. Stuff the cushion with cotton wool, be sure to fill the corners. Then glue the open edges together.
4. From the felt fabric, cut out your chosen shape, like a heart or star, and glue it to the cushion.
5. Glue on the sequins in your chosen pattern.

get cookin'

party platter

ingredients

- 1 head of lettuce
- 1 packet mozzarella cheese
- 1 packet cheddar cheese
- 1 tub low-fat soft cheese
- 1 packet edam cheese
- 2 mangoes
- 1 bunch grapes
- 2 oranges
- 2 apples
- 1 canteloupe melon

Line a large platter with lettuce leaves. Slice up the cheese and fruit and arrange it on the platter with crackers. Put the soft cheese in a small bowl in the centre of the platter.

Note: ask an adult to help with any chopping and using the oven or hob

This year the girls have really made an effort to get fit and eat right. Check out **starlet**'s healthy recipes that are super yummy too. The parents will be sooo impressed!

stuffed courgettes

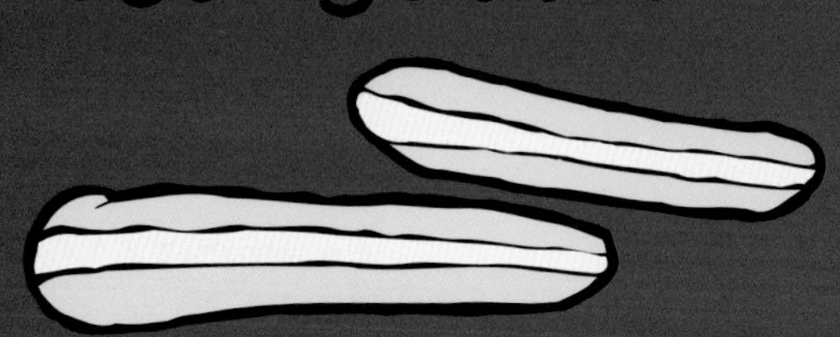

ingredients

- 3 medium courgettes
- 1 packet (120g) brown rice
- 250ml cheddar cheese, grated

1. Cut the courgettes lengthways, then scoop out the pulp and save it in a bowl.
2. Start cooking rice according to packet instructions (ask mum to help with this!)
3. Gently boil the courgettes until tender.
4. When the rice is cooked, stir in the courgette pulp and half the cheese.
5. Fill each courgette shell with the rice mixture; sprinkle the remaining cheese on top.
6. Place the filled courgettes on a greased baking tray and grill for 5 minutes or until the cheese has melted.

brainpower pocket

- 125g cheddar cheese, cubed
- 4 sticks celery
- handful of watercress
- 1 grated carrot
- 2 tins drained tuna (packed in water)
- 4 tablespoons low-fat mayonnaise
- 4 pitta breads

1. In a bowl, mix the cheese, celery, watercress and carrot.
2. Stir in the tuna and the mayonnaise.
3. Slice open one end of each pitta bread.
4. Stuff the pitta pockets with the filling.
5. Enjoy!

make the grade's study tips

If your marks aren't what they should be, or you want to raise them from good to great, check out **make the grade**'s sure-fire tips

in the classroom

Pay close attention to your teacher. Make sure you understand everything, and ask questions if you don't.

feed your brain

There's nothing worse than hunger pangs to take your mind off school. A good breakfast in the morning will set you up for the day. Choose vitamin-packed foods like fresh fruit, and tummy-warming treats like porridge to give lasting energy. Oh yeah, and don't forget lunch!

note-taking

Keep your notes neat and short. Neat notes will be easier to study. Then, experiment with styles. Highlighting pens are a good way to spice up your notes and to help make the important stuff stand out.

If you don't take notes in class then you'll have to go back to your textbook yourself and try to learn everything. When taking notes, make sure to write down the important points and details that your teacher talks about. But you don't have to write down everything your teacher says – you'll only make yourself crazy if you try to do that!

homework

It may be a drag to do homework right after school, but it really is the best time as the subjects will be fresh in your mind. Then your evenings will be free for a phone chat with your best bud and other fun stuff.

the big test

Give yourself plenty of time to prepare. Cramming at the last minute never works. Studying in a group works for some people and not so well for others. If you can talk about the subject without wandering off track to discuss your latest crush, this might be the way for you!

Help! We're moving!

Groovy Chick to the rescue ... with some top tips on how to cope with moving house

forgive the parents

Try not to get cross with your parents. They will have very good reasons for deciding to move. Talk to them about it if the idea of moving upsets you. You will need your family now more than ever since you won't have your trusty group of friends around. Remember, your parents and sibs are probably feeling nervous about the move too.

check out your new 'hood!

Break out a map, and get familiar with your new 'hood. Where do the kids hang out? Explore local parks, check out the shopping scene and ask the parents for a grand tour of the area.

where do I live again?

Memorise your new phone number and address. If you click with some super cool girl your age at the library, a simple e-mail address will do. Be careful about giving out your personal info.

embrace your new space

Start by unpacking and decorating your room. Unless it really comforts you to re-create your room exactly as it was, think of your new crib as a blank canvas you can design into the room of your dreams. Display favourite photos of your old friends in funky frames or, better yet, make a poster collage. Turn to page 26 for room makeover ideas.

where do I sign up?

Check out some activities and sports, either at school or through your local community centre. Joining a book group, netball or swim team is a great way to meet people who are into the same stuff as you.

it's gotta be you!

Don't expect to be miss popular right away. Just be yourself. Since you can't work an entire crowd, make one or two friends first and branch out from there. And don't be afraid to introduce yourself to classmates who won't always come up to you first.

stay in touch

E-mail is the easiest (and cheapest) way to stay in touch with friends back home. Set up a group list with all your buds' e-mail addresses, and write to them all at once. Check with your parents that it's OK to phone once in a while.

welcome change

Though you may not realise it now, change can be a good thing! Give your new home a chance – think of it as an adventure!

steam 'n soak

After a swim, your local pool may have a sauna and jacuzzi! Aaah! If bubbles and steam are nowhere in sight, a bubble bath at home is the next best thing. Add some bath oil, bubbles, then sit back and relax.

get movin'

Exercise may not be your idea of relaxing, but it sure will get your mind off school work and get you fit! We all know what **football babe**'s best sport is, but there are loads of other fun things you can do to get fit and feel great!

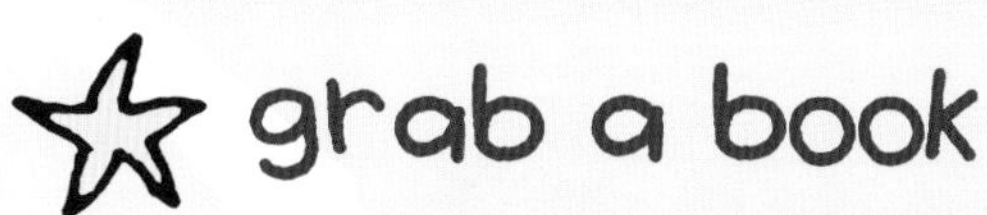

grab a book

Flop on the sofa and read... if you can't get into a juicy story, check out your fave mag... 'make it groovy' perhaps?!

school chillin'

with football babe

You've had a hard day at school, and the homework's all done. Now it's time for you and your mates to chill. Check out **football babe**'s cool ideas to relax and maybe even get fit!

stretch it out

Pop in a yoga DVD (you can borrow one from the library) and get stretchin'! Yoga's a great way to relax and it's something you can do on your own or with your mates. Lay on a couple of towels if your floor doesn't have carpet.

get creative

Turn to page 29 for some cool craft ideas, or just grab a pencil and paper and start drawing. Check out the copy draw grid on the next page to get you started.

draw football babe!

Follow the drawing on the grid opposite.

10

red face

has this ever happened to you?

On the first day of school my best mate and I were heading to the cafeteria, gushing about the new guy'. I spotted him in the first hour and couldn't stop thinking about him so I had to tell my best mate every single little detail about him. I was telling her about his gorgeous eyes and his cool skater hair when we turned the corner to see him all red-faced and staring at us like we were a couple of aliens. Now we're friends, and he always brings that up!

I was rushing through the cafeteria, trying to get the last seat at a table, when I tripped and fell, landing right in my tray of food. Everyone in the cafeteria started clapping!

For days, my little brother was bugging me to take him to the cinema. I finally agreed, and decided to invite my new crush. About half way through the movie, my little bro stands up in his chair and shouts: "Poopy time!!!!!" Everyone in the cinema started laughing, and my crush never lets me forget about it!

moments

Last summer I went to a pool party at my best mate's house. But I forgot my swimsuit, so I borrowed a spare bikini from my friend. But the bottoms were a bit too loose, and when I climbed out of the pool the bottoms slipped off!

I had to give an oral book report at school one day. As I walked to the front of the class, I accidentally farted... loud enough for half the class to hear it!

My parents and I were at a restaurant for dinner one night. Just before we left I started complaining about my maths teacher and how I didn't think she liked me very much and was kinda mean sometimes. When we left I turned around... and saw my maths teacher sitting at the table right behind me. She heard every word!

go girl's

last laugh

Amaze your mates with some super cool and super funny trivia!

did you know?

1. Butterflies taste with their feet.

2. It is possible to lead a cow upstairs... but not downstairs.

3. Elephants are the only animals that can't jump.

4. No word in the English language rhymes with 'month'.

5. Our eyes are always the same size from birth, but our noses and ears never stop growing.

6. Zzzzz... snails can sleep for three years!

7. 'Go.' is the shortest complete sentence in the English language.

8. The brain of an ostrich is smaller than its eyes.

9. A crocodile cannot stick its tongue out.

10. All polar bears are left-handed... or is that left-pawed?!

brainteasers

groovy gear wordsearch

Find all the funky fashion gear listed below in the box except for one. Write the missing word at the bottom. Oh yeah, the words in the grid may be written backwards, forwards, up, down or diagonally.

poncho rucksack cardigan bracelet beads

vest

shades

trainers

R	I	N	G	V	Z	Q	X	O	T
P	U	F	B	E	A	D	S	C	R
Q	Z	C	I	S	H	A	N	A	A
X	S	A	K	T	H	P	R	R	I
W	H	R	I	S	F	O	S	D	N
S	A	D	N	P	A	N	H	I	E
T	D	N	I	Q	A	C	L	G	R
O	E	G	Y	E	W	H	K	A	S
O	S	X	J	X	V	O	F	N	M
B	R	A	C	E	L	E	T	Z	X

dress boots bikini ring jeans

The missing word is: ....

See the solution on page 60.

Shop search

groovy chick and **starlet** are at a new shopping centre and need to find their fave shoe shop. Look at the map below and follow the clues to help them find it.

Clues:

The shoe shop is pink.
It is above a blue shop.
On the left is a green shop.
On the right is a black shop.

See the solution on page 60.

boxed-in babes

The four squares in the top left corner of the grid – showing **groovy chick**, **pop princess**, **starlet** and **hey gorgeous** – are repeated together in the same pattern once only elsewhere in the grid. Can you spot where?

See the solution on page 60.

rhyming jumble

Find the answers to the clues in the jumbled letters below. Cross off each letter as you use it.

n b t
h l s s
a d
c n
a e o c a
o e
a
s r
e o r n j
p d j h c
s
s k o

Then rearrange the letters that are left over to spell **groovy chick**'s fave buy of the last year!

- jewellery that rhymes with 'coach'
- shoes that rhyme with 'handles'
- hipster style is cool and they rhyme with 'beans'
- wear this outside; it rhymes with 'packet'
- a party outfit that rhymes with 'mess'

groovy chick's fave buy was ....

See the solution on page 60.

name the mate crossword

Answer the clues and fill in the crossword to help you guess the name of one of **groovy chick**'s best mates.

across clues:

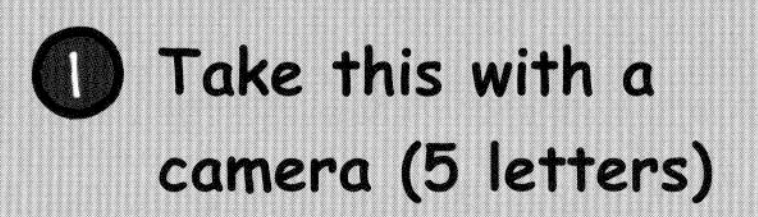

1. Take this with a camera (5 letters)
2. Use these instructions to cook something (6)
3. Wear this to go swimming (6)
4. Watch this at the cinema (5)
5. A chicken lays this (3)

down clues:

1. You might eat this at party (4)
2. Prepare for a test (5)
3. Wear this on your finger (4)
4. To ask someone to go somewhere (6)
5. The month before June (3)

groovy chick's mate is ....

Find the answer on page 60.

who's that groovy girl?

match **groovy chick** and her mates to their outfits. If you need help, everyone can be found somewhere in this annual.

write your answers here: ....

check our answers on page 60.

spot the difference

Find 10 differences between these two pictures of **groovy chick** and her mates.

Need help? Turn to page 60.

year planner 2006

Get organised with groovy chick's handy year planner! Here you can make notes of important dates, things to remember, and all those plans for parties, days out with the girls and other cool things you want to do!

bang on the door™ ©

competition

It's that time again... enter our competition and you could win some groovy stuff!

Simply send us a postcard and the first card chosen in the draw wins.

Here's what you could win:

how to enter:

1. fill out a postcard with your name, age, address and phone number
2. address the card to:
   groovy chick annual competition
   santoro graphics
   rotunda point
   11 hartfield crescent
   london sw19 3rl
3. stamp and post the card by 1st march 2006

The draw will take place on 15th march 2006.
Winners will be notified in writing by 1st April 2006.

brainteaser solutions

groovy gear wordsearch

page 50

R	I	N	G	V	Z	Q	X	O	T
P	U	F	B	E	A	D	S	C	R
Q	Z	C	I	S	H	A	N	A	A
X	S	A	K	T	H	P	R	R	I
W	H	R	I	S	F	O	S	D	N
S	A	D	N	P	A	N	H	I	E
T	D	N	I	Q	A	C	L	G	R
O	E	G	Y	E	W	H	K	A	S
O	S	X	J	X	V	O	F	N	M
B	R	A	C	E	L	E	T	Z	X

missing word is: **dress**

rhyming jumble

page 53

1. brooch
2. sandals
3. jeans
4. jacket
5. dress

(groovy chick's fave buy is: poncho)

shop search

page 51 shop number 9

name the mate crossword

page 54

boxed-in babe

page 52

who's that groovy girl?

page 55

A=3 B=4 C=2 d=1

spot the difference

page 56

stencils
See pages 24–30
61